Flying Solo

by Elizabeth Dale and Elena Napoli

FRANKLIN WATTS
LONDON • SYDNEY

Flying Solo

Contents

Chapter 1
Lift Off!

I was so excited I could hardly breathe.

The day I had been looking forward to for so long –

5 May, 1930 – was here. I was sitting in the cockpit of

my own plane, about to set off on an epic adventure!

Fingers trembling, I fastened my leather flying helmet.
I waved to the small group who'd come to Croydon
airfield to see me off. My father and my three sisters,
Irene, Betty and Molly, were all there. And so was
Lord Wakefield. He was a wealthy aircraft enthusiast,
who'd helped my father buy my plane. Well, he must
have believed in me, little Amy Johnson from Hull, even if
some of my friends and members of my flying club didn't.
How they had scoffed when I said I wanted to learn
to mend planes as well as fly them.
"That's men's work," they'd said. "You'll smell of oil and
get mucky hands."

But I didn't mind. I loved it. And I was thrilled when
I became the first woman in the world to qualify as
a ground engineer. It was then that my exciting plan
began to form ...

"Have you got everything?" yelled my father, worried.

"Yes," I called, as I double-checked: flask of tea, gun, first-aid kit, sweets, matches, spanner, life-belt and a knife in case I should fall in the sea and have to fight off sharks. I didn't have a radio, so I wouldn't be able to check the weather forecast – or call for help – if anything went wrong. I quickly pushed that thought away. It wouldn't. And if it did, as a qualified engineer, I should be able to fix it. I had my compass, watch and maps covering my route – well, most of it. Some of the route hadn't even been surveyed yet. And my thick flying jacket would just have to keep me warm despite the wind and rain that would come into my open cockpit.

Finally I was ready. A tingle of anticipation ran down my spine as I waved goodbye to my wonderful, supportive family. I started my beloved plane, *Jason*. We sped faster and faster along the runway and then we were off.

As I took to the skies, I thought about what my father had said when I first told him of my plans.

"But ... but you can't fly all the way to Australia. It's the other side of the world," he'd protested.

"Isn't that really dangerous?" Irene had asked.

"Yes, it is," I'd replied. "That's why I want to do it."

"No point trying to put her off," said Molly. "Once Amy's made up her mind, no one can stop her."

"Has anyone ever done it before, Johnnie?" asked my friend Grace, using my nickname.

"Oh, yes," I'd replied brightly. "The first time was in 1919, just after the First World War."

I wasn't going to tell them that it was done by a crew of four then, and that I planned to go solo. And that many other pilots had died or crash-landed in the jungle trying to get there.

And they'd all had far more flying experience than I had ...

But then Grace had asked, "But you won't fly on

your own, will you?"

"Oh yes, that's half the excitement," I'd said, grinning.

"Bert Hinkler flew solo and it only took him

fifteen and a half days."

"But he was a man!" cried Grace's boyfriend.

I'd laughed. "Women are just as good as men," I'd said,

"and I'm going to try to beat his record."

Chapter 2
The Challenge Begins

And here I was making good progress. Soon

the patchwork of fields below ended and I was over

the Channel. I'd left England for the first time in my life.

It was so exciting! Then, my flight across Europe

continued. After ten hours I could finally see

Vienna Airport. I had flown further than I ever had

before and the first part of my journey had been

completed successfully.

Reaching Vienna was wonderful, but that was nothing

compared to my next destination – the bustling port of

Istanbul on the very edge of Europe. As I landed, I couldn't

believe I had made it there.

I patted *Jason's* nose and smiled as I recalled

the comments of my fellow pilots:

"You'll never do it!" one had said. "You've only had

eighty-five hours' flying experience!"

"You're not up to it – you're only a girl," added another.

How I'd laughed when he said that.

When I was born in 1903, most people thought women

should know their place: staying in the house, looking after

the family, nothing more. There was no need to worry

about being educated outside the home. Well, that was

not for me! Luckily, my father agreed. He'd brought

my sisters and me up to be strong and independent.

He had supported me when I went to university and

afterwards, when I moved to London. I'd enjoyed my office

job there, but still I'd wanted more excitement. So when

I was twenty-five, I joined a flying club and learned to fly –

and absolutely loved it.

But how could I possibly make it my career?

"It's so annoying that women aren't taken seriously as pilots," I had moaned to my instructor.

"Well, you'll just have to prove how brilliant you are," he'd said, grinning.

"How?"

"Maybe by flying to Australia?" he'd joked.

From that moment on, I was determined to make it happen. And now here I was, bound for Australia.

Chapter 3
Things Start to Go Wrong

The next day, I headed further east across Asia. On my way to Baghdad, a huge sandstorm blew up. *Jason* gave a terrible lurch, his nose dipped and we dropped several thousand feet. I'd never been so frightened in my life. Sand covered my goggles, blinding me. My eyes smarted and I struggled frantically with the controls, trying to keep my plane straight.

I was so relieved when the wheels finally touched down on the desert sand. But even then the wind was incredibly strong and I still couldn't see a thing.

I frantically piled my luggage up against *Jason*'s wheels to stop him tipping over. Then I heard the sound of dogs barking and I was gripped by terror – I'd heard that desert dogs could tear people to pieces! I pulled out my pistol and stood guard by *Jason*, ready to fight off any attack.

After what seemed like hours, the storm finally died down and I was able to pack up my things, climb back inside *Jason* and fly on to Baghdad.

Luckily, we hadn't lost too much time, and on the sixth day I reached Karachi. A surprise awaited me there – a big crowd of reporters with flashing cameras. At this point in the trip, I was ahead of Hinkler's record by two whole days. I was famous!

The next day, I continued on my flight. But as I crossed

the vast plains of India, I was alarmed to see my fuel gauge

was showing empty. I needed to find somewhere to land,

and fast! I quickly scanned the landscape beneath me.

Far below was a parade ground filled with soldiers.

Desperately swerving to avoid them, I crash-landed into

a huge sign and ended up wedged between two barracks.

I climbed out of the cockpit and surveyed the smashed

wing. I couldn't believe it. I'd been on track to break

the world record, but now my adventure was over. Then

an amazing thing happened. The soldiers came racing up.

"We can fix it!" they cried.

Thanks to them, my plane was soon ready to be airborne

again. "Thank you," I called down to my soldier friends,

waving as *Jason* and I took off into the bright blue sky.

But further dangers lay ahead. *Jason* managed to carry me over a huge mountain range to Rangoon, but I landed in the middle of a monsoon. I had never seen such rain. The field I landed in was so soggy, that as *Jason*'s wheels moved slowly across it, we sank into a ditch, badly damaging the propeller and ripping *Jason*'s wing – again!

I could fix the propeller but the huge hole in the wing was another matter.

How was I ever going to obtain the materials to repair it? And how long would it take?

Suddenly I heard shouting. People were racing across the sodden field to me.

"Are you all right?" one asked.

"Can we help you?" cried another.

"It's kind of you to offer, but look!" I said, pointing in despair at the damaged wing.

"We can help," said one lady. "We are teachers and students from the local college. If we all work together, we can mend it!"

I frowned. "But we will need so much material. Where would you get it from?"

"Some of the men have shirts made from aeroplane fabric salvaged from First World War planes," said another teacher. "We could use that!"

And so they did.

It took twenty shirts altogether, but after two days *Jason* was fully repaired. After lots of thanks and many wishes of good luck, I was able to set off again.

Chapter 4
The Final Leg

The torrential rain and strong head-winds returned and my progress was very slow. I had to make many unplanned landings, one of which was in the middle of a sugar plantation. Finally, I set off on the most frightening part of my journey – two days crossing Indonesia and the shark-filled Timor Sea.

Even though I set off at six in the morning, it was night when I reached the island of Timor and too dark for me to find my planned landing strip. I flew as low as I dared, desperately peering through the pitch black, trying to find somewhere – anywhere flat – to land. At last, I saw a stretch of grass. As *Jason* bumped across it and came to a stop, we narrowly missed several huge ant heaps.

Almost immediately, we were surrounded by local tribesmen. They came running out of their huts, clutching swords, spears and knives. I was absolutely terrified. What could I do? I could only speak English – how could I possibly tell them I didn't mean them any harm? As I climbed nervously out of the cockpit, one of the men grabbed my arm.

But he was only trying to help. The tribesmen all smiled at me and led me to the nearby church, where the pastor, who fortunately spoke English, greeted me kindly and offered me a place to sleep.

As I lay in my bed that night, I was almost too excited to sleep. This would be the last night of my trip. I thought back over my adventures so far – the kind soldiers who had helped me in India, the friendly pastor here, and the students and teachers in Rangoon. What a long way I had come, flying solo around the world. I hoped my family would be proud of me.

I set off at dawn for Darwin, 500 miles away, eager to reach Australia. I flew over the Timor Sea, peering anxiously all around, and then finally I saw Melville Island, just off the Australian coast. Oh, I was so relieved. I stood up and cheered with delight, throwing overboard my inflatable pillow, which I'd carried in case I crashed into the sea. Well, I wouldn't be needing that anymore! I was so happy, I laughed and cried all the way to the Port Charles lighthouse and on towards Darwin.

I had no idea that a ship crossing the Timor Sea earlier in the day had spotted me in the air. The ship's captain had excitedly radioed the news to Darwin Airport, and several planes had set off to escort me in. But they missed me, as a strong wind had blown me off course to the west.

The escort planes finally spotted me as I approached the airport. All four flew out to greet me as I finally landed in Darwin at three o'clock in the afternoon.

DARWIN

Chapter 5
Australia at Last!

I just could not believe the tremendous welcome that awaited me. There were crowds of people, all cheering and yelling my nickname, "Johnnie! Johnnie!" as I jumped down from my cockpit.

I waved wildly back at them, hoping no one minded that I was wearing khaki shorts rather than the longer skirts normally worn by young ladies.

As the camera bulbs flashed, I quickly threw off my lifebelt and goggles and started trying to comb my wind-blown hair. What must I have looked like?

When I stepped onto Australian soil, someone called,
"Three Cheers for Amy!" and the crowd roared in reply.

I acknowledged the delightful welcome with a bow and
a smile and waited while a group of photographers
snapped photos.

As I posed for the press, I told the waiting journalists: "Tell England, my father and the rest of the world, that I am here, safe and sound and so happy."

Australian quarantine regulations demanded that a doctor must check me over to say I was healthy, but that was soon done and I was allowed to stay and celebrate. It had taken just nineteen days to fly 11,000 miles across three continents. Of course I was disappointed not to have broken the record for flying from England to Australia, but at least I'd got there alive. I was so relieved and happy.

The next day, Australian papers were full of the news, with photos of me and headlines such as, "Miss Johnson's Great Day" and "Australia's Welcome to Flying Heroine!"

Amazingly, it seemed that the news was welcomed throughout the world. I was absolutely stunned to receive a telegram from Buckingham Palace from King George V himself, which said:

The Queen and I are thankful and delighted to know of Miss Johnson's safe arrival in Australia, and heartily congratulate her upon her wonderful and courageous achievement.

To celebrate my achievement, I toured the rest of Australia. I was greeted by huge crowds wherever I went. Newsreel after newsreel showed the truly heroic welcome I was given.

Everywhere I went I was cheered and called "The Queen of the Skies". There was even a song, "Johnnie's in Town!", composed in my honour.

Thousands of people filled the streets of Sydney. Other towns and cities competed with each other for me to visit them and held grand receptions for me.

When I finally returned to England there were even more celebrations. I was greeted by another song composed especially for the occasion: "Amy, Wonderful Amy!". I was very flattered by all this attention, of course, but what I wanted most of all was to be back with my dear family. Once I saw my father and my sisters waiting for me and I hugged them again, I knew I was home.

"You made it!" my father said proudly, wiping a tear from his eye. "When I waved you off, I wondered if I would ever see you again."

"Me too!" I said, laughing and crying at the same time.

"Who'd have thought you'd actually fly all the way to Australia," cried Betty, "all on your own?"

All on my own. I smiled at her.

Still, I couldn't quite believe it. I had never felt more proud. I had flown solo to the other side of the world, navigating my way through storms and crises. I had proved that women can do anything we want to, if we put our minds to it.

Things to think about

1. How was Amy feeling as she set out on her long-awaited solo flight to Australia?
2. How did Amy's father's opinion of women differ from most people at that time? How did it help Amy in her career?
3. Why did Amy get so much attention and fame when she reached Karachi? What set-back happened on the next leg of her journey to spoil that achievement?
4. How did Darwin Airport know Amy was coming? What caused the escort planes to lose track of her?
5. What were some of the ways that people around the world celebrated Amy's success?

Write it yourself

This book retells the true story of Amy Johnson's solo flight to Australia, from Amy's point of view. Now try to write your own retelling of a different true story you know and think about the viewpoint you will tell it from. Plan your story before you begin to write it. Start off with a story map:

- a beginning to introduce the characters and where and when your story is set (the setting);
- a problem that the main characters will need to fix in the story;
- an ending where the problems are resolved.

Get writing! Try to include geographical and historical details so that your readers get a sense of the time and place of your story, and think about the dialogue your characters would use.

Notes for parents and carers

Independent reading

The aim of independent reading is to read this book with ease. This series is designed to provide an opportunity for your child to read for pleasure and enjoyment. These notes are written for you to help your child make the most of this book.

About the book

This retelling of British pilot Amy Johnson's amazing achievement in the skies portrays Amy's determination and strength in the face of a great challenge. Told from Amy's point of view, we can feel the rush as she faces real peril, never losing sight of her goal to prove her doubters wrong.

Before reading

Ask your child why they have selected this book. Look at the title and blurb together. What do they think it will be about? Do they think they will like it?

During reading

Encourage your child to read independently. If they get stuck on a longer word, remind them that they can find syllable chunks that can be sounded out from left to right. They can also read on in the sentence and think about what would make sense.

After reading

Support comprehension by talking about the story. What happened? Then help your child think about the messages in the book that go beyond the story, using the questions on the page opposite. Give your child a chance to respond to the story, asking:

Did you enjoy the story and why? Who was your favourite character? What was your favourite part? What did you expect to happen at the end?

Franklin Watts
First published in Great Britain in 2019
by The Watts Publishing Group

Copyright © The Watts Publishing Group 2019

Series Editors: Jackie Hamley, Melanie Palmer and Grace Glendinning
Series Advisors: Dr Sue Bodman and Glen Franklin
Series Designer: Peter Scoulding

A CIP catalogue record for this book is
available from the British Library.

ISBN 978 1 4451 6549 3 (hbk)
ISBN 978 1 4451 6550 9 (pbk)
ISBN 978 1 4451 7037 4 (library ebook)

Printed in China

Franklin Watts
An imprint of
Hachette Children's Group
Part of The Watts Publishing Group
Carmelite House
50 Victoria Embankment
London EC4Y 0DZ

An Hachette UK Company
www.hachette.co.uk

www.franklinwatts.co.uk